rockschool®

Debut Drums

*Performance pieces, technical exercises and in-depth guidance
for Rockschool examinations*

Acknowledgements

Published by Rockschool Ltd. © 2012
Catalogue Number RSK051219
ISBN: 978-1-908920-18-8
Revision 1 | 8 February 2013 | Errata details can be found at *www.rockschool.co.uk*

AUDIO
Recorded at Fisher Lane Studios
Produced and engineered by Nick Davis
Assistant engineer and Pro Tools operator Mark Binge
Mixed and mastered at Langlei Studios
Mixing and additional editing by Duncan Jordan
Supporting Tests recorded by Duncan Jordan and Kit Morgan
Mastered by Duncan Jordan
Executive producers James Uings, Jeremy Ward and Noam Lederman

MUSICIANS
James Arben, Joe Bennett, Jason Bowld, Larry Carlton, Stuart Clayton, Andy Crompton, Neel Dhorajiwala, Fergus Gerrand,
Charlie Griffiths, Felipe Karam, Kishon Khan, Noam Lederman, DJ Harry Love, Dave Marks, Kit Morgan, Jon Musgrave,
Jake Painter, Richard Pardy, Ross Stanley, Stuart Ryan, Carl Sterling, Henry Thomas, Camilo Tirado, Simon Troup,
James Uings, Steve Walker, Chris Webster, Norton York, Nir Z.

PUBLISHING
Fact Files written by Luke Aldridge, Jason Bowld, Neel Dhorajiwala, Stephen Lawson, Noam Lederman and David West
Walkthroughs written by Noam Lederman
Music engraving and book layout by Simon Troup and Jennie Troup of Digital Music Art
Proof and copy editing by Noam Lederman, Claire Davies, Stephen Lawson, Simon Pitt and James Uings
Publishing administration by Caroline Uings
Cover design by Philip Millard

SYLLABUS
Syllabus director: Jeremy Ward
Instrumental specialists: Stuart Clayton, Noam Lederman and James Uings
Special thanks to: Brad Fuller and Georg Voros

SPONSORSHIP
Noam Lederman plays Mapex Drums, PAISTE cymbals and uses Vic Firth Sticks
Rockschool would like to thank the following companies for donating instruments used in the cover artwork

PRINTING
Printed and bound in the United Kingdom by Caligraving Ltd
CDs manufactured in the European Union by Software Logistics

DISTRIBUTION
Exclusive Distributors: Music Sales Ltd

CONTACTING ROCKSCHOOL
www.rockschool.co.uk
Telephone: +44 (0)845 460 4747
Fax: +44 (0)845 460 1960

Table of Contents

Introductions & Information

Page

2   Acknowledgements
3   Table of Contents
4   Welcome to Rockschool Debut Drums

Rockschool Grade Pieces

Page		*CD Full Mix*	*CD Backing no Click*	*CD Backing with Click*
5	Full Rudder	1	2	3
9	Z	4	5	6
13	Rattlesnake	7	8	9
17	Big Ideas	10	11	12
21	Hazee Daze	13	14	15
25	Hoedown	16	17	18

Technical Exercises

Page		*CD Track*
28	Rudiments & Fill	19

Supporting Tests

Page		*CD Track*
29	Sight Reading	
30	Ear Tests	20–22
31	General Musicianship Questions	

Additional Information

Page		*CD Track*
32	Entering Rockschool Exams	
33	Debut Drums Marking Schemes	
34	Drum Notation Explained	
35	Drums Grade 1 Preview	23

Welcome to Rockschool Debut Drums

Welcome to Debut Drums

Welcome to the Rockschool Debut Drums pack. This book and CD contain everything you need to play drums at this grade. In the book you will find the exam scores in drum notation. The CD has full stereo mixes of each tune, backing tracks to play along to for practice and spoken two bar count-ins to the full mixes and backing track versions of the songs. There are two backing tracks for each: one with a click and one without. You can choose which one to play along with in the exam.

Drum Exams

At each grade, you have the option of taking one of two different types of examination:

- **Grade Exam:** a Grade Exam is a mixture of music performances, technical work and tests. You prepare three pieces (two of which may be Free Choice Pieces) and the contents of the Technical Exercise section. This accounts for 75% of the exam marks. The other 25% consists of a Sight Reading test (10%), a pair of instrument specific Ear Tests (10%), and finally you will be asked five General Musicianship Questions (5%). The pass mark is 60%.

- **Performance Certificate:** in a Performance Certificate you play five pieces. Up to three of these can be Free Choice Pieces. Each song is marked out of 20 and the pass mark is 60%.

Book Contents

The book is divided into a number of sections:

- **Exam pieces:** in this book you will find six specially commissioned pieces of Debut standard. Each of these is preceded by a *Fact File*. Each Fact File contains a summary of the song, its style, tempo, key and technical features, along with a list of the musicians who played on it. There is additional information on the techniques and style as well as recommended further listening. The song itself is printed on one page. Immediately after each song is a *Walkthrough*. This covers the whole song from a performance perspective, focusing on the technical issues you will encounter along the way. Each Walkthrough features two graphical musical 'highlights' showing particular parts of the song. Each song comes with a full mix version and a backing track. Both versions have spoken count-ins at the beginning. Please note that any solos played on the full mix versions are indicative only.

- **Technical Exercises:** you should prepare the exercises set in this grade as indicated. There is also a Fill test that should be practised and played to the backing track.

- **Supporting Tests and General Musicianship Questions:** in Debut Drums there are two supporting tests which are Sight Reading and Ear Tests, and a set of General Musicianship Questions (GMQs) asked at the end of each exam. Examples of the types of tests likely to appear in the exam are printed in this book. Additional test examples of both types of test and the GMQs can be found in the Rockschool *Companion Guide to Drums*.

- **Grade 1 Preview:** in this book we have included one of the songs featured in the Grade 1 Drums book as a taster. The piece is printed with its accompanying Fact File and Walkthrough, and the full mix and backing tracks are on the CD.

- **General Information:** you will find the information you need on exam procedures, including online examination entry, marking schemes and what to do when arriving (and waiting) for your exam.

We hope you enjoy using this book. You will find a *Syllabus Guide* for Drums and other exam information on our website: *www.rockschool.co.uk*. Rockschool Graded Music Exams are accredited in England, Wales and Northern Ireland by Ofqual, the DfE and CCEA and by SQA Accreditation in Scotland.

SONG TITLE: FULL RUDDER

GENRE: CLASSIC ROCK

TEMPO: 98 BPM

TECH FEATURES: BACKBEATS
BASS DRUM VARIATIONS
CONSISTENT HI-HAT PATTERN

COMPOSER: NOAM LEDERMAN

PERSONNEL: NOAM LEDERMAN (DRUMS)
STUART RYAN (GTR)
HENRY THOMAS (BASS)

♩=98 *Classic Rock*

A

OVERVIEW

'Full Rudder' is a classic rock track in the style of AC/DC, Led Zeppelin and Aerosmith. It pays homage particularly to the hard rock style of AC/DC's Phil Rudd and features backbeats, bass drum variations and a consistent hi-hat pattern among its techniques.

STYLE FOCUS

This no-nonsense style of classic rock drumming is the very definition of the phrase 'less is more'. The need to provide space for the guitars and vocals to breathe cannot be emphasised enough in this style of music. A drummer's principal responsibility in a band, after all, is to provide accurate timekeeping and a solid, consistent sound. An awareness of timing and the ability to listen to the music as well as the drums are essential in making you a well-rounded musician. A good, strong right hand technique is also important in this style of music to help sustain consistent eighth notes on the hi-hat.

THE BIGGER PICTURE

Hard rock developed as a major style in the 1970s with bands such as Led Zeppelin, Aerosmith,

Van Halen and AC/DC bringing it to the fore. The traditional hard rock sound typically consists of distorted guitars accompanied by big, heavy drums, thumping basslines and vocals that are more abrasive than those of mainstream rock.

Well-disciplined drummers are a must in hard rock because the groove has to sit perfectly within the music. If it is too fast it becomes punk; too slow and it becomes blues. Hard rock legends AC/DC have had one of the best timekeepers in the genre in the form of drummer Phil Rudd, who is also famous for his heavy hitting and unique feel. AC/DC's success has spanned from the early 1970s through to the present day. They continue to gain fans from younger generations and to inspire new hard rock bands.

RECOMMENDED LISTENING

To gain a broad view of hard rock, listen to any of AC/DC's albums. For example, *High Voltage* (1976), *Back In Black* (1980) and *Highway To Hell* (1979). *Rock In a Hard Place* (1982) by American hard rock superstars Aerosmith features the drum talents of Joey Kramer, while Van Halen's eponymous, groundbreaking debut (1978) features the 'brown snare sound' of Alex Van Halen. Check out 'Hot for Teacher' to hear some of his double-bass drum style.

Full Rudder

Tracks 1, 2 & 3

Noam Lederman

Debut Drums

Walkthrough

A Section (Bars 1–4)

This section features a classic introduction/breakdown groove. The hi-hat plays consistent eighth notes and the bass drum plays on the backbeat (the second and fourth beats of each bar). In bar 4 there is one additional bass drum and one snare on beat four that prefigures the full groove in bar 5.

Bar 1 | *4/4 time*
The time signature 4/4 indicates that there are four quarter-note beats in each bar in this piece.

Bar 1 | *Introduction groove*
The consistent hi-hat hits are all eighth notes. These can be counted as "1 & 2 & 3 & 4 &". Ensure that the strokes are even and synchronised with the click or backing track. The backbeat bass drums must be played with conviction and a secure pulse. Don't forget to allow the quarter-note rests their full length.

Bar 4 | *Preparation fill*
Although the variations in this bar are minor, they lead to the entry of the full groove in bar 5. The bass drum plays on beats one, two and three, while the snare hits only on beat four. Focus on co-ordinating effectively the bass and snare drum with the eighth notes on the hi-hat (Fig. 1).

B Section (Bars 5–12)

In this section, the groove develops and the snare is played on both backbeats (beats two and four). The bass drum follows the guitar riff and plays many offbeats. These offbeats largely follow the snare drum and are played after beats two and four of the bar. There can be a natural tendency to rush during this part so pay attention to the pulse and ensure that each snare and bass drum are played to their full length.

Bar 5 | *Offbeats*
When counting the eighth notes in the bar as "1 & 2 & 3 & 4 &", the offbeats are referred to as "&"s. It may feel less comfortable playing the offbeats than playing on the beats (1, 2, 3, 4), but it is simply a matter of practising and getting used to this slightly different feel. Playing the offbeat without the following beat can create a feeling of unevenness, which will in turn affect your timing. Use the consistent hi-hat pattern as your anchor and focus on co-ordinating the offbeat bass drums accurately.

Bar 6 | *No bass drum on beat one*
This can also feel uncomfortable at first, but if you repeat the steps outlined above it should solve the problem for you. Listening closely to the guitar and bass riffs will provide you with an understanding of the rhythmic patterns featured on the drum part.

C Section (Bars 13–20)

The feel of the groove is different in this section. The bass drum variations are played mainly on the offbeats of beats one and three, rather than on the offbeats of two and four as presented in the previous section. In bar 20, there is a final fill that ends the piece.

Bar 13 | *Offbeats of '1' and '3'*
Co-ordinating these types of offbeats in the bass drum pattern should be slightly easier than the ones you saw in section B. However, the concept should be the same and you need to focus on accuracy and timing. Listening closely to the guitar parts should assist you in playing with good synchronisation to the backing track (Fig. 2).

Bar 16 | *Togetherness*
At the end of bar 16, there are two eighth notes to be played on the snare and hi-hat. In order to achieve accuracy and fluency, aim to play these at exactly the same time. If you hear that one is played slightly before the other, try to adjust your playing until it sounds right. It is also important that both strokes are even and balanced.

Bar 20 | *Ending phrase*
This is a musical interpretation of the final guitar phrase. The hi-hat plays the first four eighth notes in the bar then rests on beats three and four. The snare hits on the first eighth note are followed by three eighth-note bass drums. The half note rest on the third and fourth beats applies to both parts of the stave, so the offbeat of the second beat is the last note you have to play here.

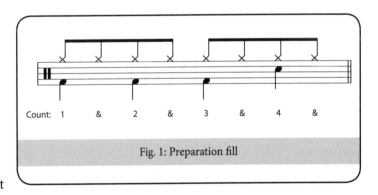

Count: 1   &   2   &   3   &   4   &

Fig. 1: Preparation fill

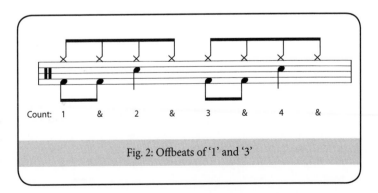

Count: 1   &   2   &   3   &   4   &

Fig. 2: Offbeats of '1' and '3'

SONG TITLE: Z
GENRE: HIP HOP
TEMPO: 90 BPM

TECH FEATURES: STRONG BACKBEAT
BASS DRUM AND HI-HAT SYNC
QUARTER-NOTE HI-HATS

COMPOSER: NEEL DHORAJIWALA

PERSONNEL: NOAM LEDERMAN (DRUMS)
NEEL DHORAJIWALA (PROD)

OVERVIEW

'Z' is a hip hop track written in the style of artists from America's West Coast scene such as Dr Dre, 2Pac (Tupac Shakur) and Snoop Dogg. By playing this track you will learn how to maintain a strong backbeat, as well as mastering bass drum and hi-hat synchronisation among other techniques.

STYLE FOCUS

The West Coast sub genre of hip hop is based on a solid quarter-note feel that is often coupled with rhythmic pianos and strings. Beats two and four (known jointly as the backbeat) are core to the groove, so snares are often combined with hand-claps to give these beats even more emphasis. Straight-feel drum parts are layered with electronic drums on top, which produces a tight sound and a 'head-nod' vibe that is the nucleus of a hip hop groove. A hip hop drummer will usually play a solid backbeat feel for the majority of the track and use fills sparingly.

THE BIGGER PICTURE

This particular form of West Coast hip hop is known as the Aftermath sound, named after super producer Dr Dre's record label Aftermath Entertainment. Dre developed the sound along with his in-house producers Mel-Man, Focus and Mike Elizondo when they moved purposely away from sample based tracks, as was common in hip hop at the time, and concentrated on using more instruments and synthesizers instead.

Countless artists can attribute their sound to the style and meticulous production of Dr Dre and his in-house stable of Aftermath producers, including rappers 50 Cent, Eminem, Snoop Dogg, Busta Rhymes and Raekwon.

RECOMMENDED LISTENING

To get to grips with the Aftermath and West Coast hip hop styles, listen to classic Dr Dre productions such as 'Still DRE', 'Xxplosive' and 'The Watcher', all of which can be found on the album *2001* (1999). 50 Cent's album *Get Rich Or Die Tryin'* (2003), The Game's *The Documentary* (2005), Eminem's *Relapse* (2009) and Busta Rhymes' *The Big Bang* (2006) are also good examples. Classic West Coast style singles include 'California Love' by 2Pac, Blackstreet's 'No Diggity' and G-Unit's 'Poppin' Them Thangs'. *Warning: these records may contain content that is unsuitable for children.*

Z

Neel Dhorajiwala

♩=90 *Hip Hop*

Walkthrough

A Section (Bars 1–4)
The opening four bars feature a basic hip hop beat with rhythmic values of quarter and eighth notes. This can feel quite challenging to play initially because there is only one backbeat snare in each bar.

Bar 1 | *One backbeat*
In most hip hop beats you will hear two backbeat snare hits in each bar, on the second and fourth beats. However, in this groove there is only one backbeat, which is played on the fourth beat in the bar. The bass drum is played on every beat apart from the fourth beat. Ensure that this unorthodox voicing does not affect the consistency of the pulse (Fig. 1).

Bar 4 | *One added snare*
In the last bar of this section, there is one additional snare hit on the third beat. This variation adds movement to the groove and prepares you for the next section in bar 5.

B Section (Bars 5–12)
Here the groove develops with consistent eighth notes on the hi-hat. The snare is played on both backbeats and there are variations in the bass drum pattern. Changing rhythms in your lead hand can affect your timing and synchronisation with the backing track. Practise the hi-hat pattern in sections A and B with a metronome to help you understand the rhythmic change and maintain a consistent pulse.

Bar 5 | *Two backbeats*
The snare is played on both backbeats (second and fourth beats) throughout this section. Playing two backbeats in each bar should feel more comfortable than the one, so you can focus on the bass drum variations and secure co-ordination of your three limbs. This is a good opportunity for you to check if your posture is balanced and that you can reach the bass drum pedal comfortably (Fig. 2).

Bars 11–12 | *Bass drum and snare variations*
You will need to perform the written variations in the bass drum and snare parts while maintaining an even hi-hat pattern. It might be a good idea to break this section down into individual bars. Try practising each bar a few times, focusing on the minor variations in each bar until it feels comfortable. When you feel ready, put it all together and build up your speed if necessary.

C Section (Bars 13–16)
This is the breakdown section of the song. The bass drum and snare patterns are similar to section A but the hi-hat plays quarter notes instead of eighth notes. In bar 16 there is a simple but effective hip hop fill that uses eighth notes on the hi-hat and quarter notes on the bass drum.

Bar 13 | *Playing quarter notes*
This bar may look straightforward on the page but it can be challenging to play well. Practising bars 12 and 13 repeatedly with a click will help you overcome this challenge.

Bar 16 | *Quarter-note rests*
This bar consists of solid eighth notes on the hi-hat and quarter note bass drums on the first and third beats of the bar. Between the bass drum notes you will see the symbol for a quarter-note rest. This means that nothing is being played there apart from the hi-hat (on the top part of the stave).

D Section (Bars 17–21)
The final section of the piece features a similar groove and variations to the ones you saw in section B. The piece ends with one quarter-note stroke on the hi-hat and bass drum.

Bars 17–20 | *Unison*
It is necessary to play two, three and, sometimes, four limbs together when drumming. Your goal is to move your limbs in perfect time in order to hit the surface of the drums or cymbals to produce a unison sound. Here there are only two types of unison: hi-hat + snare and hi-hat + bass drum. Practise both on the kit to improve your unison playing.

Bars 18 | *Two consecutive snares*
When playing two consecutive snare strokes, keep the dynamic level balanced by lifting your hand to the same height before hitting the drum both times. The hi-hat keeps constant eighth notes, so make sure your hands don't clash.

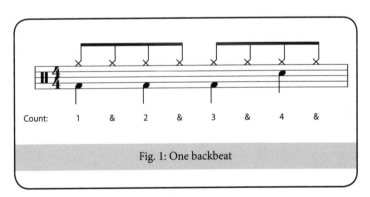

Fig. 1: One backbeat

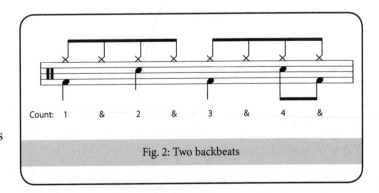

Fig. 2: Two backbeats

SONG TITLE: RATTLESNAKE

GENRE: INDIE

TEMPO: 89 BPM

TECH FEATURES: BASS DRUM VARIATIONS

HEAVY BACKBEAT

FILLS

COMPOSER: PETER HUNTINGTON

PERSONNEL: STUART RYAN (GTR)

HENRY THOMAS (BASS)

NOAM LEDERMAN (DRUMS)

OVERVIEW

Fans of punk-influenced indie rock and garage groups like The Strokes, The Hives and The Datsuns will be interested in the track 'Rattlesnake', which features bass drum variations, a heavy backbeat and fills among its techniques.

STYLE FOCUS

This style of rock is about simplicity, energy and attitude. The drum pattern will invariably lock into the guitar riff to give the whole track plenty of percussive punch. Fills are used sparingly, if at all. Try to keep your time keeping steady – don't be tempted to rush – and play with unwavering commitment to the backbeat. The snare hits need to be heard through the overdriven guitars, so this is no time to be gentle.

THE BIGGER PICTURE

The MC5 and Iggy And The Stooges led the charge that burst out of the economic collapse and social discontent of Detroit in the late 1960s. They were punk before the name was ever applied to their music: simple rock 'n' roll played at furious volumes. In this type of garage rock it didn't matter if you couldn't play your instrument well as long as you played it with a suitable level of aggression.

Modern bands influenced by punk revisited the garage rock mind set. For example, The Strokes' back to basics approach, along with The Hives' manic intensity and the next generation of Detroit rockers The Von Bondies and The White Stripes. All of these bands played rock stripped down to its essentials of simple chord structures and plenty of attitude. Chris Dangerous of The Hives brings a machine-like consistency to his band, playing few fills and powering the tracks along with unrelenting energy and a devotion to keeping the beat.

RECOMMENDED LISTENING

The birth of garage rock came with the release of MC5's live debut album *Kick Out The Jams* (1969) and The Stooges' self-titled debut (1969) that contained the blistering lo-fi track 'No Fun'. Garage rock was a big influence on Dangerous' stripped-down, aggressive drumming with The Hives on the tracks 'Walk Idiot Walk' from *Tyrannosaurus Hives* (2004) and 'Hate To Say I Told You So' from *Veni Vidi Vicious* (2000). 'Harmonic Generator' from The Datsuns' eponymous debut (2002) is another recent example of garage rock's influence.

Rattlesnake

Peter Huntington

♩=89 *Indie*

Walkthrough

A Section (Bars 1–4)

The piece starts with a full and heavy indie rock groove. There are consistent eighth notes on the hi-hat, snare drum on each backbeat (beats two and four), and various bass drum hits. Note that there is one eighth-note rest in the middle of bar 2.

Bar 1 | *Groove*

It is important to play the eighth note hi-hats accurately and to synchronise them with the rhythm guitar part. Next, you must focus on the bass and snare drum parts. Remember that these are a combination of quarter notes and eighth notes. The bass drum plays on beats one and three as well as the offbeats of three and four. Practising this bass drum pattern with the backbeat snare is a good way to start working on this groove (Fig. 1).

Bar 2 | *Eighth-note rest*

The eighth-note rest in this bar is placed on the third beat. Because it is notated in the bottom part of the stave, the hi-hat above it should still be played. A good tip for instances such as this is to always use the most consistent limb/part as your anchor. In this case it is the hi-hat, so as long as you keep the hi-hat even and co-ordinate the variations well this will sound convincing.

B Section (Bars 5–12)

In this section, there are various snare and bass drum variations. However, apart from these changes in the groove you will notice how the hi-hat pattern isn't always consistent. Counting the eighth notes in each bar throughout this section will help you to perform this accurately.

Bar 8 | *When the hi-hat stops*

The main challenge in this bar lies in the fact that you can no longer rely solely on the eighth note hi-hats as your anchor because the last two eighth notes are missing. This is the time for you to develop a solid pulse that many drummers refer to as the internal clock. Counting "1 & 2 & 3 & 4 &" while you practise is the best way of developing this internal clock, but you will also need a metronome to help you keep the pulse consistent. Try practising this hi-hat pattern without the snare and bass drum until it is accurate and comfortable.

Bar 12 | *Rhythmic values*

As well as this section's break in the hi-hat pattern, there is also a combination of two rhythmic values here: quarter notes and eighth notes. You need to understand the rhythm being played in this bar: "1 (& 2 &) 3 & 4 &". It is still necessary to count and not miss the offbeats of one and two in order to remain in sync with the backing track. The first stroke in this bar is the only time in the piece where you will

have to play three drum voices in unison. Make sure that all three parts are hit at the same time and that the following quarter-note rest is observed (Fig. 2).

C Section (Bars 13–20)

The drum groove and variations continue to follow the guitar riffs in this section.

Bar 14 | *Bass drum and snare variations*

While maintaining an even hi-hat pattern, you will need to perform the written variations in the bass drum and snare parts. Try practising the bass and snare drum pattern without the hi-hat until it feels comfortable and before bringing in the hi-hat pattern.

Bar 16 | *Lonely backbeat*

This is the only bar in the piece where the backbeat is played without the support of the hi-hat. Ensure that your timing is accurate and the snare sounds convincing. Remember, the backbeat snare is a quarter note so allow it its full length when playing this bar.

Bar 20 | *Ending phrase*

This is a musical interpretation of the final guitar phrase. The hi-hat plays the first four eighth notes in the bar then rests on beats three and four. The snare hits on the second eighth note and the bass drum on the remaining three. The half note rest on the third and fourth beats applies to both parts of the stave, so the offbeat of the second beat is the last note you have to play here.

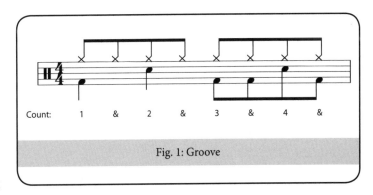

Fig. 1: Groove

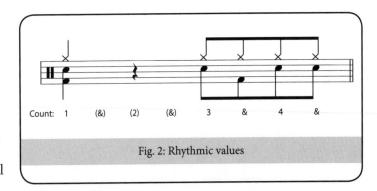

Fig. 2: Rhythmic values

SONG TITLE: BIG IDEAS

GENRE: POP

TEMPO: 89 BPM

TECH FEATURES: OFFBEAT BASS DRUM
EIGHTH-NOTE REST
BASS & SNARE UNISON

COMPOSER: JON MUSGRAVE
& KUNG FU DRUMMER

PERSONNEL: JON MUSGRAVE (PROD)
NOAM LEDERMAN (DRUMS)

OVERVIEW

'Big Ideas' is written in the style of boy bands similar to Take That, Westlife and Boyzone. It features simple patterns, smooth grooves and aspects of R'n'B among its varied techniques.

STYLE FOCUS

There is nothing flash in 'Big Ideas'. With pop acts the drummer is there simply to play for the song and to support the vocals. Pop is about catchy hooks, melodies that stick in your head and a beat that people can dance to. To be a good pop drummer you need to find the groove and sit as deeply in the pocket as possible. Your drumming needs to be tasteful and uncluttered. The snare will typically fall on the '2' and '4' of the bar to make it easy for audiences to clap in time to the music, but there is also room for creating syncopation (playing off the beat) on the bass drum. Your hi-hat playing needs to be slick and smooth to make sure the rhythm flows under the melody.

THE BIGGER PICTURE

Pop can be a dirty word for some musicians, but the genre is full of talented songwriters and great players. The British charts were dominated by many boy bands in the 1990s, and the most successful of those bands filled stadiums and sold millions of albums – a feat that is rarely seen in other genres of music. Many boy bands are 'created' by managers and record labels and, as such, there will be often be a legion of songwriters behind the scenes crafting their hits; although some bands, such as Take That, co-write much of their own material.

There are some terrific session drummers who make their living backing the biggest pop stars, both in the studio and live: Donavan Hepburn, who tours with Take That; Karl Brazil, who has played with Robbie Williams; and Steve Barney, who has recorded with Will Young and The Sugababes.

RECOMMENDED LISTENING

Take That's 2006 comeback album *Beautiful World* contains elegantly crafted contemporary pop. The singles 'Patience' and 'Shine' are great examples of modern pop drumming. Westlife are one of the most successful groups in the history of British pop. Their self-titled debut (1999) was immaculately produced and headed up by the single 'Flying Without Wings'. Boyzone's 1998 album, *Where We Belong* (1998), shifted millions thanks to its blend of R'n'B and pop.

Big Ideas

Jon Musgrave & Kung Fu Drummer

♩=90 *Pop*

Debut Drums

Walkthrough

A Section (Bars 1–8)
The piece starts with a flowing pop beat featuring consistent eighth notes on the hi-hat, snare drum on each backbeat (beats two and four) and various bass drum hits. There are two additional eighth notes on the snare drum in bar 8 that prefigure the change in the groove introduced in bar 9.

Bar 1 | *Groove*
It is important to play the eighth note hi-hats accurately and to synchronise them with the rhythm guitar part. Next, focus on the bass and snare drum parts. Remember that these parts are a combination of quarter notes and eighth notes. The bass drum plays on beats one and three as well as the offbeat of three. Practising this bass drum pattern with the backbeat snare is a good way to start working on this groove.

Bar 4 | *Eighth-note rest*
The eighth-note rest in this bar is placed on the third beat. It is notated in the bottom part of the stave, which means the hi-hat above it should still be played. A good tip is to use the most consistent limb/part as your anchor (in this case, the hi-hat). As long as you keep the hi-hat even and co-ordinate the variations well this will sound convincing (Fig. 1).

Bar 8 | *Snare fill and unison*
Apart from playing the backbeats, the snare drum should hit on the offbeats of beats three and four to create three consecutive snare drum strokes that form the basis of more advanced drum fills you will find in higher grades. Remember the concept of unison here because playing the drum voices exactly together will create accurate time and consistent synchronisation with the backing track. Pay attention to the three-limb hit on beat four because this is the only place in the piece that you will have to perform this.

B Section (Bars 9–12)
This is the breakdown section of the piece, which is common in modern pop chart hits. The hi-hat remains as consistent eighth notes but the bass and snare drum patterns develop throughout the section.

Bars 9–11 | *Moving the snare*
The snare part in this section is as follows:
  Bar 9: no snare
  Bar 10: snare on beat four
  Bar 11: snare on beat three
Ensure that moving the snare does not affect your timing and that each quarter note is played fully. The consistent hi-hat pattern can be your anchor here.

Bar 12 | *Consecutive bass drums*
There are three consecutive eighth note bass drums in this bar played between the two backbeat snares. Maintain a steady pulse and ensure that these three eighth notes are even to produce a solid groove.

C Section (Bars 13–20)
The drum groove and variations in this section are similar to the ones in section A. However, there are more eighth-note rests and a short ending phrase in bar 20.

Bars 13–19 | *Bass drum and snare variations*
You will need to perform the written variations in the bass drum and snare parts while maintaining an even hi-hat pattern. Try practising the bass and snare drum pattern without the hi-hat until it feels comfortable and even before introducing the hi-hat pattern.

Bar 14 | *Offbeat bass drum*
Apart from playing at the beginning of the groove, the bass plays the offbeats of the second and third beats in this bar. The offbeats are the second eighth note in each beat, most commonly counted as '&'. When emphasising the offbeats there may be a tendency to play ahead of the track, but if you listen carefully to the click this should not happen.

Bar 20 | *Ending phrase*
The hi-hat plays the first two eighth notes in the bar then rests on beats two, three and four. The snare hits on the first eighth note and the bass drum on the second. This is followed by a quarter-note rest and a half note (minim) rest. As the rests apply to both parts of the stave, the offbeat of the first beat will be the final note of the piece (Fig. 2).

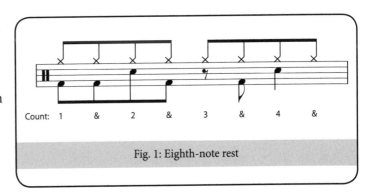

Fig. 1: Eighth-note rest

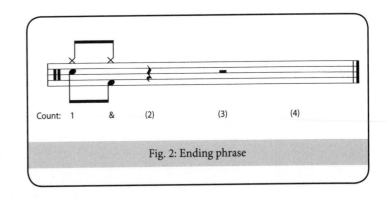

Fig. 2: Ending phrase

SONG TITLE: HAZEE DAZE

GENRE: FUNK

TEMPO: 92 BPM

TECH FEATURES: BASS & SNARE UNISON
QUARTER-NOTE RESTS
TWO CONSECUTIVE SNARES

COMPOSER: LUKE ALDRIDGE

PERSONNEL: STUART RYAN (GTR)
HENRY THOMAS (BASS)
NOAM LEDERMAN (DRUMS/PERCUSSION)
ROSS STANLEY (KEYS)
JAMES ARBEN (FLUTE)

OVERVIEW

'Hazee Daze' is a funk track in the style of acts like Jamiroquai, James Taylor Quartet and US3 that leans towards the acid jazz or jazz funk sub-genres. It features unison snare and bass hits, eighth-note rests and offbeat bass drum notes.

STYLE FOCUS

Watch out for the intro to 'Hazee Daze': the hi-hat plays on the backbeat ('2' and '4') but once the groove gets going in the second line, the main pulse is performed as quavers on the hi-hat. The bass drum plays with the snare in places to add some weight.

Typically of jazz funk or acid jazz, 'Hazee Daze' features a more complex chord progression than most funk tunes. The piano part is particularly jazzy.

THE BIGGER PICTURE

Jazz funk was born in the late 1960s when musicians such as Miles Davis and Herbie Hancock began using funk grooves a basis for compositions and vehicles upon which to improvise. The genre developed throughout the 1970s, eventually losing much of its earthy, funky qualities, gaining in their place sophisticated harmonies and slick studio production that was typical of its time.

The late 1980s was the era of acid jazz. This sub-genre was named after the Acid Jazz record label renowned for releasing records that harked back to the classic jazz funk of the 1970s with a modern twist.

Acid jazz enjoyed a revival in the 1990s with the James Taylor Quartet, US3 and Jamiroquai achieving commercial success with their own unique blends. The style featured in the charts and was played on a variety of radio stations from Radio 1 to Jazz FM, such was the crossover appeal of the music.

RECOMMENDED LISTENING

Jamiroquai's first album, *Emergency On Planet Earth* (1993), has more of an old school funk feel, whereas their subsequent album *Travelling Without Moving* (1996) betrays a disco influence. Herbie Hancock's *Head Hunters* (1973) and *Man-Child* (1975) are great examples of keyboards leading an ensemble. Maroon 5 are a more modern example of a funk-influenced band who feature keyboards in their line-up. Their debut, *Songs About Jane* (2002), is worth listening to.

Hazee Daze

Luke Aldridge

Debut Drums

22

Walkthrough

A Section (Bars 1–4)

This A section is the intro. It consists of quarter notes on the hi-hat and bass drum. There is a short snare drum fill in bar 4 that leads to the full groove in bar 5.

Bar 1 | *Quarter notes*

In the opening bar, the bass drum plays quarter notes on beats one and three and the hi-hat plays quarter notes on beats two and four. All quarter notes should be even and played in synchronisation with the backing track (Fig. 1).

Bar 1–4 | *Quarter-note rests*

There are many quarter-note rests in this section, but as long as you understand the pattern and remember to count the beats in each bar this should not be too challenging to perform. Remember that in drum notation the various drum voices are divided between the upper and lower parts of the stave. So whenever you feel that a certain pattern looks difficult, you can break it down and practise each part individually. As always, it is important to count the rests and allow the full length of each rest, otherwise the timing might be affected.

Bar 4 | *Two consecutive snares*

When performing two consecutive snare strokes it is important to ensure that the dynamic level is balanced. This can be done by lifting the hand that plays the snare to the same height before hitting the drum. Remember that there is a quarter note hi-hat to play at the same time, so make sure that your hands do not clash.

B Section (Bars 5–12)

In this section the groove develops with consistent eighth notes on the hi-hat. The snare is played on both backbeats (beats two and four) and there are variations in the bass drum pattern. Changing rhythms in your leading hand can affect your timing and synchronisation with the backing track. However, after the change from quarter notes to eighth notes in bar 5 the hi-hat pattern remains consistent until the end of the piece.

Bar 5 | *Backbeat unison*

The backbeat is played on the snare drum throughout this section and it is important that both hands hit the drum or cymbal at precisely the same time. If you feel that one is being played before the other, try lifting your hand more and co-ordinate its movement so that both hands reach the drum or cymbal surface at the same time.

Bar 6 | *Backbeat unison with bass drum*

In the fourth beat of this bar the hi-hat, snare and bass drum should all be played together. The backbeat unison principle that was explained above can be implemented here,

too. However, playing three parts with exact timing and co-ordinating hands and feet can be more challenging, so be patient and give your body time to learn the movement.

Bars 7–12 | *Bass drum and snare variations*

Maintaining the even hi-hat pattern will help you to perform the written variations in the bass drum and snare parts. It might be useful to break this section down into individual bars. Try practising each bar a few times, focusing on the minor variations in each until it feels comfortable to play.

C Section (Bars 13–20)

Apart from a busier pattern, there is an eighth-note rest to consider in bar 16 and the ending phrase/fill in bar 20.

Bar 16 | *Eighth-note rest*

In this bar the eighth-note rest is placed on the third beat. As notated in the bottom part of the stave, the hi-hat above it should still be played. A good tip is to always use the most consistent limb/part as your anchor. In this case, this is the hi-hat. Therefore, as long as you keep the hi-hat even and co-ordinate the variations well this part should sound convincing (Fig. 2).

Bar 20 | *Ending phrase*

This is probably the most challenging bar in the entire piece. It is recommended that you practise the bottom part of the stave separately before adding the hi-hat once you are comfortable. Remember the unison concept and ensure that all eighth notes are even and consistent.

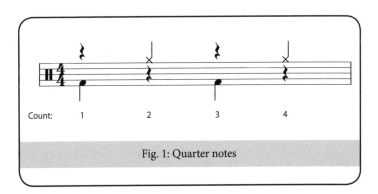

Fig. 1: Quarter notes

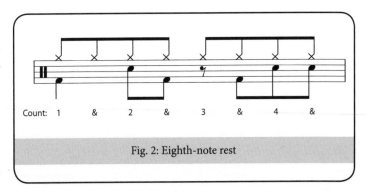

Fig. 2: Eighth-note rest

SONG TITLE: HOEDOWN
GENRE: COUNTRY
TEMPO: 100 BPM

TECH FEATURES: QUARTER-NOTE RESTS
SNARE DRUM VARIATIONS
BASS DRUM VARIATIONS

COMPOSER: HENRY THOMAS

PERSONNEL: STUART RYAN (GTR)
HENRY THOMAS (BASS)
NOAM LEDERMAN (DRUMS)
ROSS STANLEY (KEYS)
FELIPE KARAM (VIOLIN)

OVERVIEW

'Hoedown' is written in the style of modern country artists such as Shania Twain, Dixie Chicks, Garth Brooks and Keith Urban. The track features a steady backbeat as well as snare and bass drum variations among its techniques.

STYLE FOCUS

Traditional country put the spotlight on the singer and the lyrics. Contemporary country takes the original style and updates it with slicker production and a more modern sound. It retains its identity by employing standard country instrumentation – steel guitars, violins, banjos – but reinforces it with a strong backbeat, electric guitars and keyboards. Country drummers all play for the song and it has never been a genre for those who long to hog the limelight. At high tempos, country is dancing music so keep it steady and bright. Ballads should be played in a more restrained style to give the vocalist room to soar.

THE BIGGER PICTURE

Country is the music of the southern states of America. It was originally referred to as hillbilly or old time music and became a substantial influence on the birth of rock 'n' roll and rockabilly.

Buddy Harmon learned his trade as the house drummer at Nashville's Grand Ole Opry and helped define the style of country drumming on hundreds of sessions with country legends including Patsy Cline, Johnny Cash and a young Elvis Presley.

In the 1970s, many big artists drew upon the southern musical heritage. For example, The Band and their country-influenced drummer Levon Helm. Contemporary country made its presence felt on both sides of the Atlantic with Billy Ray Cyrus' smash hit 'Achy Breaky Heart' in the early 1990s. The success of his country single was later built upon by Shania Twain, Garth Brooks and Dixie Chicks.

RECOMMENDED LISTENING

Dixie Chicks' *Wide Open Spaces* (1998) features the hit 'There's Your Trouble', a contemporary country classic, while their 2006 album *Taking The Long Way* features Chad Smith of the Red Hot Chili Peppers laying down country grooves. New Zealander Keith Urban is arguably the reigning king of contemporary country and his album *Love, Pain & The Whole Crazy Thing* (2006) straddles country, rock and pop.

Hoedown

Henry Thomas

♩=100 *Country*

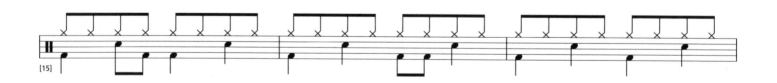

Walkthrough

A Section (Bars 1–2)
The introduction section is only two bars long in this piece. It consists of quarter note hi-hats on the backbeat (beats two and four), bass drum, which is played mostly on beats one and three, and one snare hit in bar 2.

Bar 1 | *Quarter notes*
In the opening bar, the bass drum plays quarter notes on beats one and three and the hi-hat plays quarter notes on beats two and four. All the quarter notes should be even and played in perfect synchronisation with the backing track.

Bars 1–2 | *Quarter-note rests*
There are many quarter-note rests in these bars, but as long as you understand the pattern and remember to count all the beats, including the rests, this shouldn't be too challenging. Remember, in drum notation the various drum voices are divided between the upper part and lower part of the stave. Whenever you feel that a certain pattern looks difficult you can break it down and practise each part individually.

B Section (Bars 3–10)
In this section, the groove develops with consistent eighth notes on the hi-hat. The snare is played on both backbeats (beats two and four) and there are variations in the bass drum pattern. Changing rhythms in your leading hand can affect your timing and synchronisation with the backing track. However, after the change from quarter notes to eighth notes in bar 3, the hi-hat pattern remains largely consistent until the end of the piece.

Bars 3–10 | *Bass drum and snare variations*
You will need to perform the written variations in the bass drum and snare parts while maintaining an even hi-hat pattern. Break this section down into individual bars. Try practising each bar a few times, focusing on the minor variations in each until it feels comfortable.

Bar 8 | *Two bass, two snare*
There are two bass drums followed by two snares in the second part of this bar. The hi-hat maintains the consistent eighth-note pattern and can be used as the anchor. Aim to play both bass drum and snare drum notes at the same dynamic level. Your natural tendency will be to play the second one in each group softer (especially the snare), but this can easily be solved if you lift your hand to the same height both times.

Bar 10 | *Shifting the anchor*
The main challenge in this bar lies in the fact that you can no longer rely exclusively upon the eighth note hi-hats as your anchor because the last two eighth notes are missing. You can, however, shift your focus to the snare drum, which

is played on both eighth notes and can therefore be relied upon to maintain a solid pulse. Try practising this hi-hat pattern without the snare and bass drum until it is accurate and comfortable (Fig. 1).

C Section (Bars 11–20)
The groove feels slightly different in the first five bars of this section. This is because the bass drum variations are played on many offbeats. From bar 17, the groove returns to a straighter feel similar to the one you played in section B. The final phrase of the piece is played in bar 20.

Bar 11 | *Bass drum offbeats*
When counting the eighth notes in the bar as "1 & 2 & 3 & 4 &", the offbeats are all referred to as the "&"s. It might feel less comfortable playing the offbeats than playing on the beats (1, 2, 3, 4). However, it is just a matter of practising and getting used to this slightly different feel.

Bar 20 | *Ending phrase*
This is a musical interpretation of the final guitar and violin phrase. The hi-hat plays the first four eighth notes followed by a quarter note on beat three. Apart from the backbeat (beat two) played on the snare, all the other strokes that need to be co-ordinated with the hi-hat are played with the bass drum. The quarter-note rest on the fourth beat applies to both parts of the stave, so the hi-hat and bass drum hit on the third beat will be the final note of this piece. (Fig. 2).

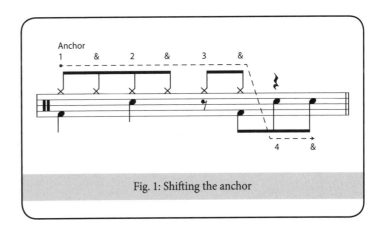

Fig. 1: Shifting the anchor

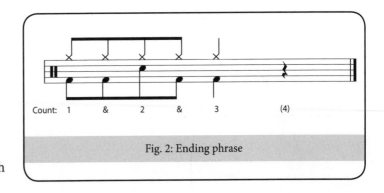

Fig. 2: Ending phrase

Technical Exercises

In this section the examiner will ask you to play a selection of exercises drawn from each of the three groups shown below. In addition there is a Fill exercise which you will play using the designated backing track on the CD. You do not need to memorise the exercises (and can use the book in the exam) but the examiner will be looking for the speed of your response.

The stickings shown (L & R) are there as a guide for right handed drummers. Left handed drummers should reverse the sticking patterns. Before you start the section you will be asked whether you would like to play the exercises along with the click or hear a single bar of click before you commence the test. Groups A–C should be played at ♩=70.

Group A: Single Strokes
In eighth notes

Group B: Double Strokes
In eighth notes

Group C: Paradiddles
Single paradiddle in eighth notes

Group D: Fill
In the exam you will be asked to play the three bar groove shown followed by one of the notated fills chosen by the examiner. You will perform this exercise to the backing track on the CD. The tempo is ♩=80.

Sight Reading

You will be asked to prepare a sight reading test which will be given to you by the examiner. The test is four bars long and played on the snare drum. The examiner will allow you 90 seconds to prepare it and will set the tempo for you. The tempo is ♩ = 80.

There are two ear tests in this grade. The examiner will play each test to you twice. You will find one example of each type of test printed below.

Test 1: Fill Playback and Recognition

The examiner will play you a one bar fill in common time played on the snare drum. You will play back the fill on the snare drum. You will then identify the fill from two printed examples shown to you by the examiner. You will hear the test twice.

Each time the test is played it is preceded by a one bar count in. There will be a short gap for you to practise. Next you will hear the vocal count in and you will then play the fill to the click. The tempo is ♩ = 70.

Test 2: Groove Recall

The examiner will play you a two-bar groove played on the bass drum, hi-hat and snare. This is a two bar-bar groove repeated. You will hear the test twice. You will be asked to play the groove back on the drum voices indicated for four bars.

Each time the test is played it is preceded by a one bar vocal count-in. The tempo is ♩ = 80.

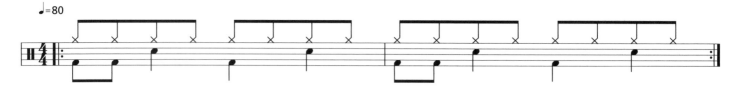

General Musicianship Questions

In this part of the exam you will be asked five questions. Four of these questions will be about general music knowledge and the fifth question will be asked about your instrument.

Music Knowledge

The examiner will ask you four music knowledge questions based on a piece of music that you have played in the exam. You will nominate the piece of music about which the questions will be asked.

In Debut, you will be asked to identify:

- Drum voices on the stave

- Quarter note and eighth note values

Instrument Knowledge

The examiner will also ask you one question regarding your instrument.

In Debut you will be asked to identify:

- The following parts of the drum kit – bass drum, snare, high tom, medium tom, floor tom, hi-hat, ride cymbal and crash cymbal

Further Information

Tips on how to approach this part of this exam can be found in the *Syllabus Guide* for Drums, the Rockschool *Drums Companion Guide* and on the Rockschool website: *www.rockschool.co.uk*.

Entering Rockschool Exams

Entering a Rockschool exam is easy. You may enter either online at *www.rockschool.co.uk* or by downloading and filling in an exam entry form. Information on current exam fees can be obtained from Rockschool online or by calling +44 (0)845 460 4747.

- You should enter for your exam when you feel ready.

- You may enter for any one of the three examination periods shown below with their closing dates:

EXAMINATION PERIODS

PERIOD	DURATION	CLOSING DATE
Period A	1st February to 31st March	1st December
Period B	1st May to 31st July	1st April
Period C	23rd October to 15th December	1st October

These dates apply from 1st September 2012 until further notice

- The full Rockschool examination terms and conditions can be downloaded from our website. The information shown below is a summary.

- Please complete your entry with the information required. Fill in the type and level of exam and instrument, along with the examination period and year. Paper entry forms should be sent with a cheque or postal order (payable to Rockschool Ltd) to the address shown on the entry form. Entry forms sent by post will be acknowledged either by letter or email, while all entries made online will automatically be acknowledged by email.

- Applications received after the expiry of the closing date, whether made by post or online, may be accepted subject to the payment of a late fee.

- Rockschool will allocate your exam to a specific centre and you will receive notification of the exam showing a date, location and time, as well as advice on what to bring to the centre. We endeavour to give you four weeks notice ahead of your exam date.

- You should inform Rockschool of any cancellations or alterations to the schedule as soon as you can because it may not be possible to transfer entries from one centre, or one period, to another without the payment of an additional fee.

- Please bring your music book and CD to the exam. You may use photocopied music if this helps you avoid awkward page turns. The examiner will sign each book during each examination. Please note, you may be barred from taking an exam if you use someone else's music.

- You should aim to arrive for your exam 15 minutes before the time stated on the schedule. Guitarists and bass players should get ready to enter the exam room by taking their instrument from its case and tuning up. This will help with the smooth running of each exam day.

- Each Debut exam is scheduled to last 15 minutes. You can use a small proportion of this time to set up and check the sound levels.

- You will receive a copy of the examiner's marksheet two to three weeks after the exam. If you have passed you will also receive a Rockschool certificate of achievement.

Debut Drums Marking Schemes

ELEMENT	PASS
Performance Piece 1	12+ out of 20
Performance Piece 2	12+ out of 20
Performance Piece 3	12+ out of 20
Technical Exercises	9+ out of 15
Sight Reading	6+ out of 10
Ear Tests	6+ out of 10
General Musicianship Questions	3+ out of 5
TOTAL MARKS	**60%+**

PERFORMANCE CERTIFICATE | DEBUT

ELEMENT	PASS
Performance Piece 1	12+ out of 20
Performance Piece 2	12+ out of 20
Performance Piece 3	12+ out of 20
Performance Piece 4	12+ out of 20
Performance Piece 5	12+ out of 20
TOTAL MARKS	**60%+**

Drums Notation Explained

BASS DRUM & TOMS

Bass drum   Floor tom   Medium tom   High tom

SNARE

Snare   Ghost snare   Rim-shot   Cross stick   Buzz snare

Strike snare drum and surrounding rim at same time   *Place palm on snare drum head and strike rim with stick*

HI-HAT

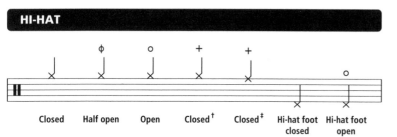

Closed   Half open   Open   Closed†   Closed‡   Hi-hat foot closed   Hi-hat foot open

† *Used on the first closed hi-hat that follows an open hi-hat*

‡ *The hi-hat is closed without being struck. Note that the hi-hat closed (cross) symbol may appear above drum voices other than the hi-hat (as shown above). This simply means another drum voice is being played at the same moment that the hi-hat is being closed.*

OTHER CYMBALS

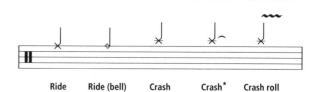

Ride   Ride (bell)   Crash   Crash*   Crash roll

***Allow all cymbals to ring on** unless explicitly stopped, as indicated by the keyword **'Choke'**. Occasionally ties may be used (*) to emphasise that cymbals should be allowed to ring on. This can avoid confusion during syncopations and pushes.*

GENERAL MUSIC NOTATION

Accentuate note (play it louder).

Slashes are used to demarcate bars during solos, fills, developments and other ad lib. sections.

D.%. al Coda
Go back to the sign (%) then play until the bar marked ***To Coda*** ⊕ then skip to the section marked ⊕ ***Coda***.

Repeat the bars between the repeat signs.

D.C. al Fine
Go back to beginning of song and play until bar marked ***Fine*** (end).

When a repeated section has different endings, play the first ending only the first time and the second ending only the second time.

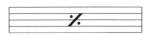
Repeat the previous bar. In higher grades these may also be marked *sim.* or *cont. sim.*

Repeat the previous two bars. In higher grades these may also be marked *sim.* or *cont. sim.*

In rudiments, each stem slash subdivides the note value by half.

MUSICAL TERMS WITH SPECIFIC EXAMINATION DEFINITIONS

Fill   Play an individual, stylistic fill.

Develop   Extend the musical part in a stylistically appropriate manner.

Cont. sim.   Continue in similar way but vary the pattern slightly.

Rit. (ritardando)   Gradually slow the tempo.

SONG TITLE: KAISER ROLL
GENRE: INDIE ROCK
TEMPO: 115 BPM

TECH FEATURES: CRASH HITS
OPEN HI-HAT
MOVING BETWEEN CYMBALS

COMPOSER: NOAM LEDERMAN

PERSONNEL: STUART RYAN (GTR)
HENRY THOMAS (BASS)
NOAM LEDERMAN (DRUMS/
PERCUSSION)

OVERVIEW

'Kaiser Roll' is written in the style of mod-influenced British indie groups including Blur, Kaiser Chiefs and Ocean Colour Scene. It should be played with the energy of rock and its techniques include open hi-hat and moving between cymbals.

STYLE FOCUS

This style of drumming takes its lead from mod music of the late 1970s and early 1980s. Mod drummers had more finesse than their punk peers and looked to the grooves of northern soul for inspiration. Rick Buckler of The Jam could power a track like "A' Bomb In Wardour Street' with as much energy as a punk drummer, but he could easily groove like a Motown drummer on songs such as 'Town Called Malice'. Steve White, who played with Paul Weller in The Style Council and later solo, is a master of soul and R&B influenced rock who frequently uses accents on his hi-hat to add a pulse to his grooves.

THE BIGGER PICTURE

Even though their music was faster and tougher, The Jam were inspired by their forefathers The Who,

The Small Faces and The Kinks. Later in the band's career, their music had a touch of northern soul as well as punk as their catchy, guitar driven songs boasted memorable hooks and driving drum beats.

The Jam's frontman Paul Weller turned his back on the mod scene when he formed The Style Council, only to return to the fold in the 1990s with acclaimed albums *Wild Wood* (1993) and *Heavy Soul* (1997).

The Kaiser Chiefs picked up where The Jam ended with a sound dominated by crunchy guitars. Later, the band replaced their punk influences with pop sensibilities inspired by the great British bands of the 1980s, especially Madness.

RECOMMENDED LISTENING

The Kaiser Chiefs' debut album *Employment* (2005) boasts two standout songs: 'Oh My God' and 'I Predict A Riot'. For Motown-influenced mod drumming, listen to Rick Buckler on the The Jam's hit 'Town Called Malice' from their final album *The Gift* (1981). Weller's album *Stanley Road* (1995), featuring the single 'The Changingman', is a mod classic with drumming from Steve White. Lastly, Ocean Colour Scene's 'The Day We Caught The Train' is a good example of this style from indie's Britpop era.

Kaiser Roll (Grade 1 Preview)

Noam Lederman

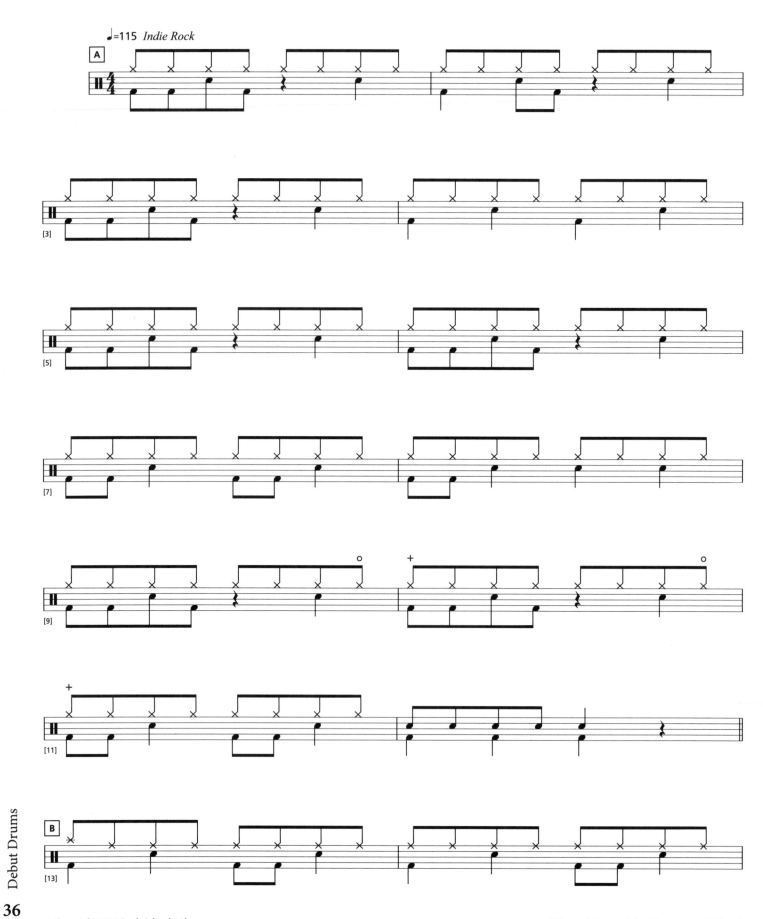

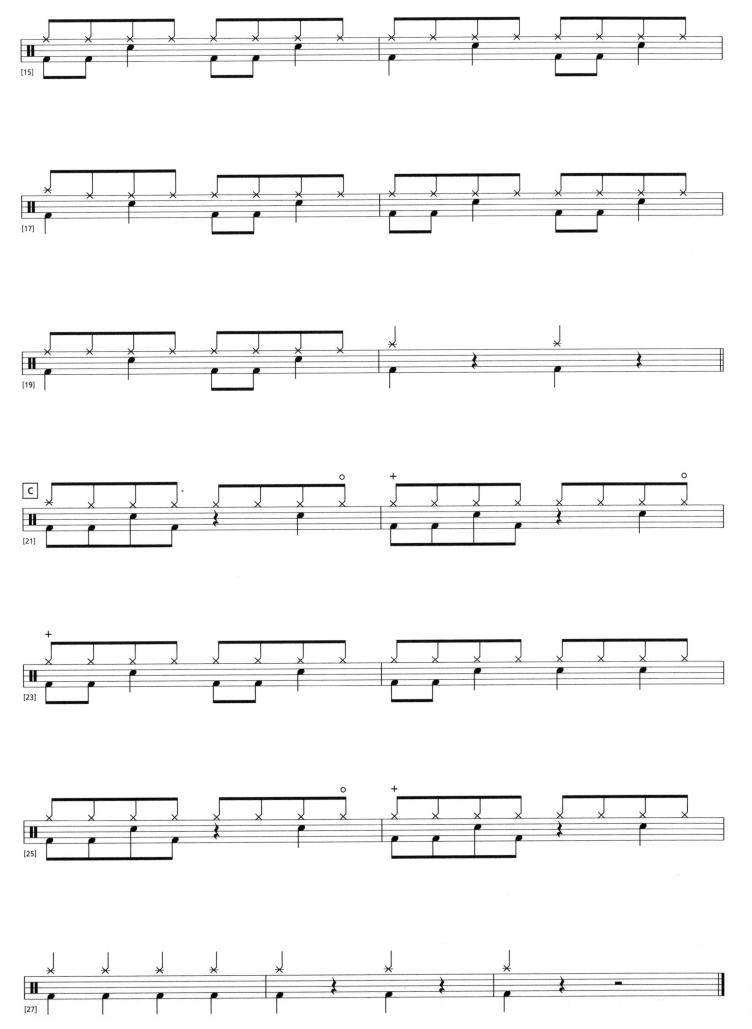

Walkthrough (Grade 1 Preview)

A Section (Bars 1–12)

This is the A section of the piece which, in most rock songs, is referred to as the verse. The groove is introduced straight away with eighth note hi-hats, backbeat snare and a varied bass drum pattern. The open/closed hi-hat is added from bar 9 and there is a snare/bass drum fill in bar 12.

Bars 1–4 | *Groove*

The snare and bass drum pattern follows the guitar riff, so pay attention to what is played on the track. Isolating each beat and focusing upon the bass drum pattern is a good starting point when working on this section. On beat one there are two consecutive bass drums to play. Remember that these must be performed evenly and, as long as you focus on the balance and do not stop the natural bounce of the bass drum beater, this should be achieved.

Bar 1 | *Quarter-note rest*

In the third beat of the bar there is a quarter-note rest. This means that nothing will be played at the bottom part of the stave. However, the hi-hats notated above the rest should be played. These will also help you maintain a steady and consistent pulse.

Bar 5 | *Note values*

There are two rhythmic note values used in this bar: quarter notes and eighth notes. Remember that quarter notes are counted as "1 2 3 4" and eighth notes as "1 & 2 & 3 & 4 &".

Bar 9 | *Open hi-hat*

The small circle above the hi-hat note means that the hi-hat should be played in the open position. This open hi-hat sound is created by loosening the hi-hat pedal and hitting the hi-hat at the same time. In order to play open hi-hat in time you will need to co-ordinate the movement of your hi-hat foot with your hand that plays the hi-hat. Your hi-hat foot should stay in contact with the pedal because removing it will affect your posture, balance and timing. Avoid leaning backwards, sideways or forwards (Fig. 1).

Bar 10 | *Closed hi-hat*

The '+' sign above the first hi-hat note indicates the hi-hat should be played in the closed position. This is achieved by pressing the hi-hat pedal down with your foot and tightening the hi-hat cymbals. As with the open hi-hat, you will still need to hit the hi-hat with your hand at the same time. This movement must be timed well or else the closed hi-hat will still sound like an open (or half open) hi-hat.

Bar 12 | *Snare and bass fill*

In this bar, there is a drum fill that indicates the end of the A section and the beginning of the B section in bar 13. The bass drum plays three consecutive quarter notes and rests on beat four. This needs to be co-ordinated with the snare pattern, which includes four eighth notes followed by a quarter note. There are two sticking options for this snare fill: alternate sticking starting with your leading hand (R L R L R) or play all strokes with your leading hand (R R R R R). Whichever sticking option you decide to use, ensure that the rhythms are accurate and co-ordinated well with the bass drum (Fig. 2).

B Section (Bars 13–20)

This is the second section of the piece, usually referred to as the chorus in rock music. The groove is played on the ride cymbal with a few crash cymbal hits.

Bar 13 | *Crash cymbal*

The first cymbal note in this bar indicates the crash cymbal should be played. Co-ordinating the crash with the bass drum is an important and useful skill for every drummer.

Bar 13 | *Ride cymbal*

Apart from the crash hits, all the cymbal notes in this section tell you that the ride cymbal should be played. The ride will replace the natural part of the hi-hat in the groove and should be played with accuracy and in unison.

Bar 20 | *Crashing*

In this bar, there are two crash hits played with the bass drum. These are placed on beats one and three with quarter-note rests in between. To ensure you perform the crash and bass drum in unison, hit the crash with conviction and continue to count the beats during the rests.

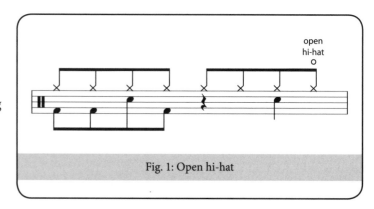

Fig. 1: Open hi-hat

Fig. 2: Snare and bass fill